LONE WOLF and CUB

by

GOSEKI KOJIMA

cover by
FRANK MILLER
and
LYNN VARLEY

第7巻

小島剛夕　小池一夫

C000077964

FIRST
PUBLISHING

Kazuo Koike
STORY

Goseki Kojima
ART

Frank Miller
COVER ILLUSTRATION & INTRODUCTION

David Lewis, Christine M. Martine, Alex Wald
ENGLISH ADAPTATION

Willie Schubert
LETTERING

Paul Guinan
PRODUCTION

Rick Oliver
EDITOR

Rick Obadiah
PUBLISHER

Alex Wald
ART DIRECTOR

Kathy Kotsivas
OPERATIONS DIRECTOR

Rick Taylor
PRODUCTION MANAGER

Kurt Goldzung
SALES DIRECTOR

Lone Wolf and Cub (Kozure Okami) © 1987 Kazuo Koike and Goseki Kojima.

English translation © 1987 First Comics, Inc. and Global Communications Corporation.

Cover illustration and introduction © 1987 Frank Miller.

Published monthly in the United States of America by First Comics, Inc., 435 N. LaSalle, Chicago Il 60610, and Studio Ship, Inc. under exclusive license by Global Communications Corporation, Musashiya Building, 4th Floor, 27-10, Aobadai 1-Chome, Meguro-Ku, Tokyo, 153 Japan, owner of world wide publishing rights to the property Lone Wolf and Cub.

Lone Wolf and Cub #7 (ISBN 0-915419-16-5) © 1987 First Comics, Inc. and Global Communications Corporation. All rights reserved.

First printing, November 1987.

I t was a mad time. The Shogun's every wild whim became law, enforced by penalty of death. Teachings of Buddha against violence and cruelty were twisted into edicts against the killing of animals of every kind, bringing famine and pestilence to Japan's once-thriving farmlands. Hunters and trappers crowded the streets of disease-ridden towns, turning to begging and crime.

It was a time of moral decay and ridiculous pageantry, a time of stupid death and meaningless sorrow.

Lord Asano was young, and had little patience with the etiquette of corruption in the Shogunate. He refused to pay a court official a bribe. The official tricked Asano into wearing the wrong pants to a ceremony where taking a step out of time was cause for public humiliation. In a rage, Asano attacked his enemy. Before he was subdued, Asano heaved his sword the length of a corridor of Tokugawa Castle, the Shogun's own home.

He missed his mark. His sword pierced an ornate golden sliding door. For ruining the door, Asano was summarily ordered to die by ritual suicide.

Forty-seven of Asano's retainers sought revenge, and failed. The Shogun granted them the privilege of following their master to death by harakiri. Forty-seven samurai warriors, too many to contain in a single courtyard or temple, brought daggers to their bellies and slumped forward as the executioner's blade cut through their necks.

The tale of the Forty-Seven Loyal Retainers is a study in the conflict between samurai ethics and Shogun bureaucracy. To the samurai, devotion to his Lord transcended any other passion in his life. This obligation to obey and serve his master unquestioningly and fearlessly was the centerpiece of the samurai code. It was called *giri*.

Giri demanded utter loyalty also to one's family name and one's friends, and even to strangers to whom one felt sympathy in the most poetic of ways.

Itto Ogami, hero of Kazuo Koike's and Goseki Kojima's *Lone Wolf and Cub*, has no master and no family name left to honor. His giri is to his son, his mission of vengeance, and, at times, to total strangers.

Frank Miller
Los Angeles 1987

PLEASE NOTE: I suffered a case of cross-cultural dyslexia while preparing my introduction to *Lone Wolf and Cub* #6. The first sentence of paragraph three should have read, "He shifted his grip and shoved the blade to the <u>left</u>."

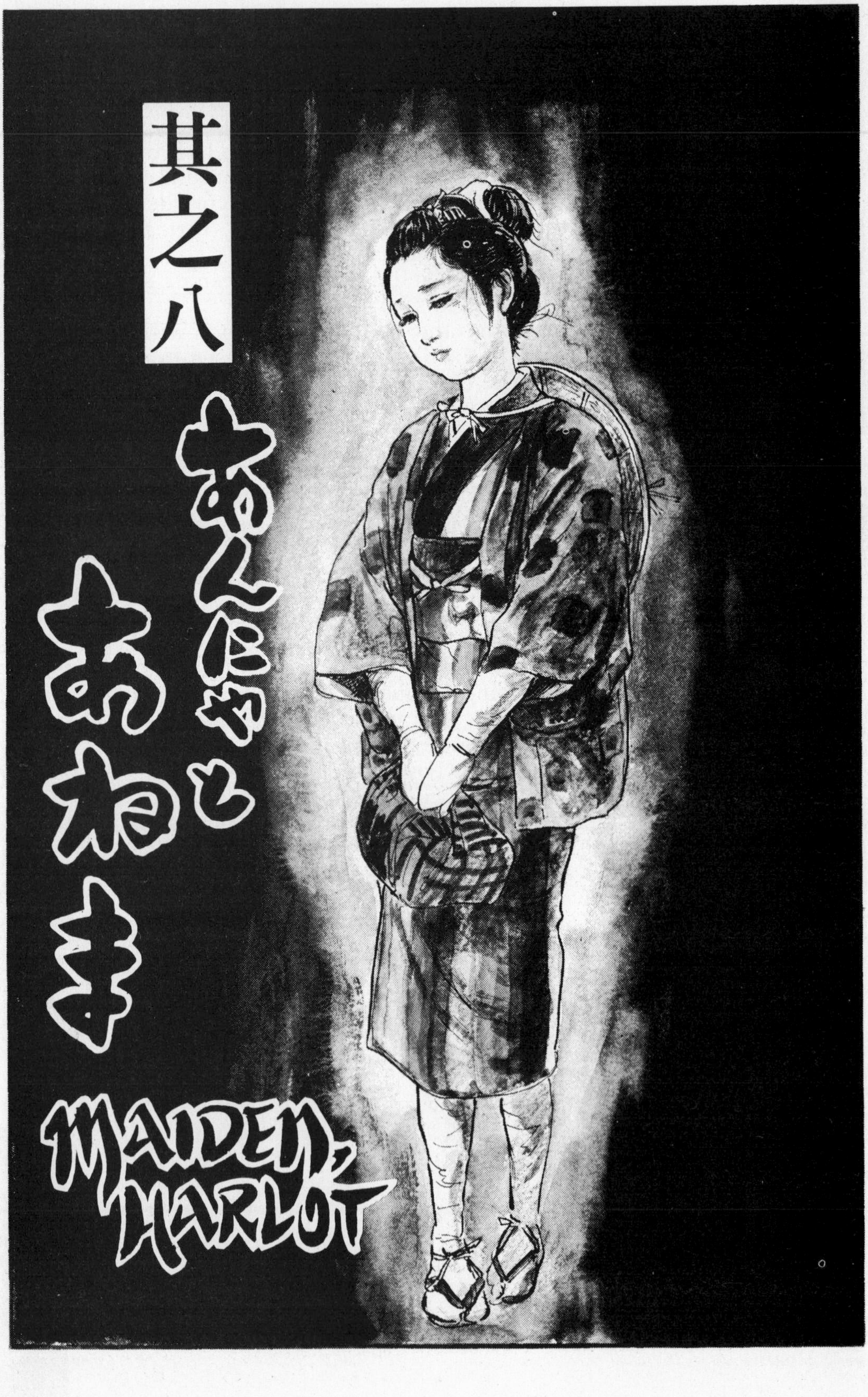
其之八
あんにゃと
あねま
MAIDEN,
HARLOT

A RIVER ON THE UTSUNOMIYA BYWAY.

香取
鹿島廻り
宇都宮みち
板久宿に近く

（板久は潮来とも書く）

2

3

Kosotaku, Mayataku:
These travellers' prayers
 shall you write in your heart.
Best chant them each morning
 ere you depart.
Then no harm
 shall come to you.

Morning travellers,
  rise with the dew.
Travellers by night,
  keep ginger to chew.

Be wary of strangers
met on the way.
Spend nights alone for
safe journey by day.

Riders remember--
  your horse won't trip holes.
If first you take caution
  to write "south" on your soles.

8

Rub salt on your feet,
  warm them well near the fire.
Treat with shoyu* or sesame
  when at last you retire.

*SHOYU--SOY SAUCE.

WELL! THAT SHOULD DO IT.

NOW WARM YOUR FEET BY THE FIRE.

LIKE THIS.

AH!

IT'S BEEN A LONG TIME SINCE I'VE TASTED A *VIRGIN*.

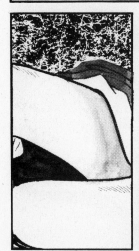

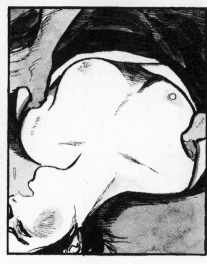

11

HUH.
HUH.
HUH.

GASP!

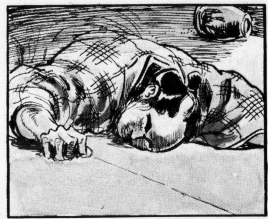

AH!

14

EEEEEEK! CRASH!

SOMEBODY COME QUICK!

thap thap thap

UH-HUH-
WAAAAH!

WAH-
HAAAA!

SIS--
YOU'RE
BLEED-
ING.

LOOK! IT'S *NAGGING MATSU*, THE "PRINCESS BUYER!" HE'S A FAMOUS *PIMP!*

HE'S A GENIUS AT HAGGLING PRICES. I'VE HEARD HE'S THE BEST.

HE WON'T HAGGLE ANYMORE WITH HIS *TONGUE* BITTEN OFF. HE'S FINALLY *CHOKED* ON IT.

NAGGING MATSU ALWAYS KEPT HIS HANDS *OFF* THE GOODS. I'LL BET SOME *STREET GIRL* WAS IN HERE AFTER THE *RECEIPTS...*

RIGHT. SOME GIRL HE'D KICKED OUT.

FIND THE GIRL! SHE CAN'T BE FAR AWAY!

YOU GO TELL THE *KIOROSHI* GANG WHAT'S HAPPENED! ASK THEM IF WE SHOULD *ARREST* HER OR NOT.

YES SIR!

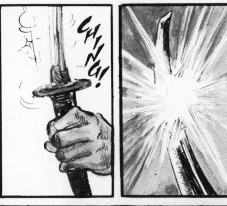

CHING!

thap
thap

OFFICIAL
BUSINESS!
OPEN
UP!

SHWOCK!

I, UH... SORRY TO INTRUDE.

THERE'S BEEN A *MURDER.* WE'RE SEARCHING FOR THE GIRL WHO DID IT.

NOT HERE.

JUST IN CASE...

WE'D LIKE TO BE SURE.

INDEED. AND WHAT IF YOU *DON'T* FIND THIS CRIMINAL?

*RONIN--A MASTERLESS SAMURAI.

WHA--?

SHWOCK!

WHY IT'S JUST A--

HE'S BEING PUNISHED.

NOW... HOW ABOUT THAT HEAD.

GET OUT!

Y-YE-YE-YES!

23

TH-
THANK
YOU.

YOU'D BETTER
GO OUT BY
THE BACK GATE.
ESCAPE ALONG
THE LEDGE
BETWEEN THE
WALL AND THE
MOAT.

WE EACH HAVE OUR
OWN ROAD TO FOLLOW,
DAIGORO. EVEN THIS
GIRL HAS A ROAD
SHE MUST WALK
BY HERSELF.

24

THERE IS A TIME FOR FORTUNE, A TIME FOR MISFORTUNE. A TIME TO LIVE AND A TIME TO DIE. WE COULDN'T GO ON WITHOUT THAT THOUGHT.

LISTEN WELL, DAIGORO. HER ROAD IS HER OWN. THOUGH IT MAY *SEEM* CRUEL, ALL OUR AID WOULD BE IN *VAIN.*

GO NOW AND BE CARE-FUL.

BYE, SIS.

THANK YOU.

THERE SHE IS!

HOLD IT!

DAMN WHORE!

WE'VE GOT YOU NOW, BITCH!

26

STAND *GUARD* OUTSIDE THIS RONIN'S ROOM. NO FOOLISHNESS, NOW!

YES MA'AM.

I AM *TORIZO*, BOSS OF THE *KIOROSHI* GANG. THE PROCURERS AND PLEASURE HOUSES OF *BOSHU* ARE UNDER MY CONTROL.

HMF!

THIS CHILD WAS *PURCHASED* BY NAGGING MATSU, ONE OF MY PROCURERS. SHE IS OUR *ANEMA*.*

SHE BELONGS TO US. I *DEMAND* THAT YOU HAND HER OVER.

*ANEMA-A GIRL SOLD TO A BROTHEL, BUT STILL A VIRGIN.

28

clack

I REFUSE.

29

SAMURAI-- THE WORLD OUTSIDE CALLS US THE *BOHACHI*.

DO YOU UNDERSTAND?

EXPLAIN YOURSELF.

BOHACHI-- THOSE WHO *FORGET* THE EIGHT *VIRTUES*. FILIAL PIETY, RESPECT FOR ELDERS, LOYALTY, HONESTY, DUTY, MANNERS, MODESTY, SHAME. THESE MEAN *NOTHING* TO US.

WE ARE *YAKUZA!* WE SCOFF AT THE WORLD'S SHAME.

*YAKUZA-- SHUN THE OUTSIDE. A GANGSTER.

YOU HAVE NOTHING TO GAIN BY *OPPOSING* US. NOTHING--WHETHER YOU WIN OR LOSE. A SAMURAI LOSES NO FACE BY *RETURNING* A GIRL TO HER *OWNERS.* PLEASE HAND HER OVER.

BESIDES SHE'S A *CRIMINAL.* SHE *MURDERED* NAGGING MATSU.

I SAID I *REFUSE!*

THE O-IHAI* MEANS NOTHING TO YOU NOW! IT'S NOTHING MORE THAN A SHARD OF WOOD! YOU ARE NO LONGER A CHILD OF THE OUTSIDE WORLD--NOT FROM THE MOMENT WE BOUGHT YOU!

*O-IHAI-- A MORTUARY TABLET TO REMEMBER A DEPARTED RELATION.

ARE YOU GOING TO SET UP YOUR O-IHAI IN THE MIDST OF THE PLEASURE QUARTERS? ARE YOU GOING TO *PRAY* TO IT DAY AND NIGHT IN A *BROTHEL?* THAT'S NOT PERMITTED FOR AN *ANEMA* LIKE YOU.

OR ARE YOU FOOL ENOUGH TO TRY TO *BUY* A SAMURAI'S *PITY?*

THE BOSS IS RIGHT! YOU'RE AN ANEMA NOW! DON'T FORGET-- NAGGING MATSU *PAID* FOR YOU!

YOU STILL DON'T *UNDERSTAND,* DO YOU?

I...

COME ON, NOW. I'LL *CLEAR* YOU WITH THE OFFICIALS FOR KILLING MATSU.

A FEW *BRIBES* DON'T BOTHER ME. AS LONG AS I GET MY MONEY'S WORTH OUT OF YOU.

YOU'RE TRYING MY PATIENCE, GIRL!

IF YOU *REFUSE* TO COOPERATE, THEN THE SAMURAI AND HIS SON--

MUST *DIE* ON YOUR ACCOUNT!

IT'S THE *CODE* OF THE BROTHEL NOT TO BRING TROUBLE UPON DECENT FOLK.

YOU'VE BEEN PAID FOR WITH A *PIMP'S* SILVER. YOU, TOO, MUST LIVE BY THE CODE!

STOP DRAGGING YOUR ASS! GET OVER HERE NOW!

35

SO YOU WON'T HAND OVER THE CHILD?

NEVER!

AFTER EVERYTHING I'VE SAID YOU STILL DON'T UNDERSTAND? DON'T BE A FOOL! WHY RISK YOUR *LIFE* AND THAT OF YOUR SON FOR A MISERABLE ANEMA? WHAT IS SHE TO YOU?

THAT TABLET WAS NO *ORDINARY* O-IHAI! IT WAS A MEMENTO FROM PARENT TO CHILD, TORN ASUNDER WHILE YET THEY LIVED!

A FORLORN MEMORIAL OF *LIVING DEATH!* A CHILD AND HER PARENTS, NEVER TO MEET AGAIN IN THIS FLOATING WORLD! AN *OATH* NOT TO HATE HER PARENTS, FORCED TO SELL HER BY HOPELESS *POVERTY!* NEVER TO PART WITH IT, ALWAYS TO PRAY TO IT. FILIAL PIETY WE NO LONGER KNOW, STRADDLING THE *SIX WAYS* AND THE *FOUR BIRTHS* OF THE WORLD!*

ONLY WE WHO TRAVEL THE DARK ROAD OF *HELL*-- ONLY *WE* CAN *SAVE* HER!

I SAW HER O-IHAI-- AND UNDERSTOOD. THAT'S REASON ENOUGH TO TAKE HER SIDE.

*THE SIX WAYS OF THE BUDDHIST WORLD-- THE WAY OF HELL, THE WAY OF THE DEMON, THE WAY OF THE BEAST, THE WAY OF SLAUGHTER, THE WAY OF MAN, THE WAY OF HEAVEN. THE FOUR BIRTHS-- BIRTH OF WOMB, BIRTH OF EGG, BIRTH OF WATER, BIRTH OF TRANSFIGURATION.

SAMURAI! *YOU* MAY LIVE BY THE SIX WAYS AND THE FOUR BIRTHS. BUT EVEN WE KUTSUWA OF THE FLOATING WORLD HAVE OUR *FACE* TO PRESERVE! LET'S *DEAL!*

THE GIRL IS AN *ANEMA* UNTIL SHE TAKES HER *FIRST* CUSTOMER. WE GET A GOOD *PRICE* FROM MEN WHO'LL PAY TO DEFLOWER A VIRGIN.

I'D LIKE *YOU* TO DEFLOWER HER, SAMURAI. *TAKE HER* AND I'LL ALLOW HER TO GO *FREE.*

NEVER.

IN THAT CASE, THERE'S ONLY ONE OTHER WAY. THE TORTURES OF THE KUTSUWA!

BUT IF SHE *SURVIVES* I WILL *FREE* HER.

FAIR ENOUGH. BUT *I* WILL TAKE THE PUNISHMENT IN HER PLACE.

B- BUT...

YOU HAVE NO RULES AGAINST SUBSTITUTES.

THE *FRIENDS* OF AN AILING PROSTITUTE MAY TAKE HER PLACE IN THE TORTURES.

AND IF WE *KILL* YOU, SAMURAI?

FOR GENERATIONS THE KUTSUWA OF KIOROSHI HAVE BEEN *LED BY WOMEN*. FROM ALL YOU HAVE SAID--AND LEFT *UNSAID*--I SEE THE REASON WHY.

I'M *HONORED*, SAMURAI.

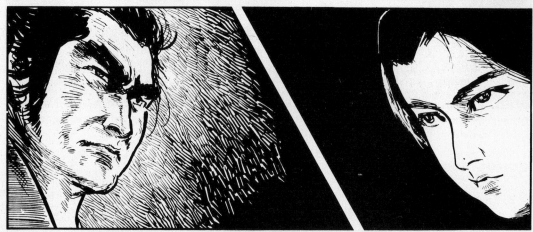

B-BUT SAMURAI-- YOU MUSTN'T--

BEGIN!

CREAK
CREAK

SPLASH!

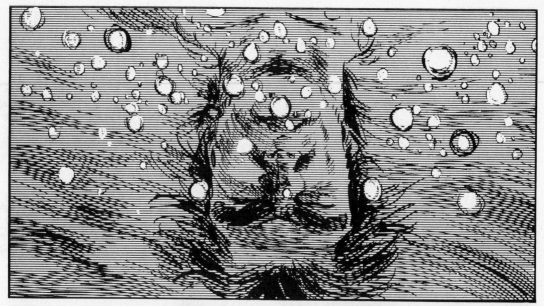

WHETHER AS SYMBOLIC RE-BIRTH, OR AS CRUEL *AMUSEMENT*, TORTURE BY *WATER* WAS THE FAVORED PUNISHMENT OF THE PLEASURE QUARTERS. BEGINNING WITH THE ZODIACAL *HOUR* UNDER WHICH THE PROSTITUTE WAS BORN, THE DUNKING CONTINUED THROUGH THE 12 SIGNS UNTIL HER OWN CAME AROUND AGAIN.

FOR EACH SIGN, SHE WAS PLUNGED INTO THE WATER, AND HELD THERE UNTIL HER BREATH GAVE OUT.

ENOUGH! NEXT THE *BURIBURI!*

READY! *BURIBURI!*

49

BURIBURI!

BURIBURI!

BURIBURI WAS THE *HARSHEST* TORTURE OF THE *HARLOT*. *SPUN* HEADFIRST FROM THE *RAFTERS*, THE WOMAN WAS *BEATEN* WITH BAMBOO SPLINTS. AT EACH STROKE, THE KUTSUWA GANGSTERS WHO CONTROLLED THE PLEASURE QUARTERS SHOUTED TOGETHER THE CHANT "BURIBURI," TAKEN FROM THE SOUND OF THE SPINNING VICTIM. ONLY LOSS OF CONSCIOUSNESS, OR *DEATH* BROUGHT THE TORTURE TO AN END.

BURIBURI!

BURIBURI!

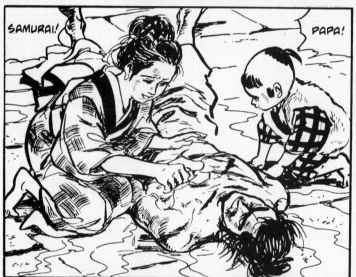

SAMURAI!

PAPA!

FOR ME... HE DID IT FOR *ME*... SAMURAI...

A *TRUE* SAMURAI. THERE AREN'T MANY LEFT.

HE'S THE REAL THING, BOSS. GOOD WITH HIS *SWORD*, BUT STRONGER WITH HIS *SPIRIT*. WE WERE MORE AFRAID THAN HE WAS!

THERE. I'VE *BURNED* THE *CONTRACT.* YOU'RE *FREE,* CHILD. GO HOME TO YOUR VILLAGE.

I—

WE LIVE *APART.* THE DUTIES AND OBLIGATIONS OF THE FLOATING WORLD MEAN NOTHING TO US.

DON'T WORRY ON OUR ACCOUNT. GO.

TH-THANK YOU FOR EVERYTHING.

UNH!

DAIGORO. SEE HER OFF.

TO THE DAY I DIE, I- I'LL NEVER...

MY BUSINESS IS NOT YET OVER.

AT LAST! I *THOUGHT* YOU HAD *ANOTHER* MOTIVE.

INDEED.

YOU'RE NO ORDINARY MAN. YOU CAME TO KIOROSHI PLEASURE QUARTERS FOR A *REASON*...

YOU SAID YOU LIVE *APART* FROM THE SIX WAYS AND THE FOUR BIRTHS--IN *MEIFUMADO*, THE WORLD OF *DEATH* AND THE PATH OF *DEMONS*. I'VE HEARD OF YOU. YOU'RE--

THE *ASSASSIN*-- THE *LONE WOLF* WITH *CUB!*

YOU'VE COME FOR MY LIFE?

I KNOW I'M NOT YOU'RE *MATCH*, BUT I'LL *FIGHT* YOU TO MY *DYING BREATH*.

NO.

53

WHAT HAVE YOU DONE?

THE *DYING REQUEST* OF THE WRECK OF A WOMAN-- AN *ANNYA*, A HARLOT WHO SPENT HALF A LIFETIME IN THE KIOROSHI, WAS *DRIVEN* FROM ITS DOORS WHEN *SICKNESS* FELLED HER.

KILL THE *ANNYA-HINA*, SHE SAID THE *HARLOT DOLLS* OF THE MARCH FESTIVAL.

THE *HAIR* OF THE ANNYA-HINA IS THE HAIR OF *DEAD* PROSTITUTES. THE *ROBES* OF THE ANNYA-HINA ARE *MEMENTOS* OF THE WOMEN WHO DIED.

THE *HATRED* OF DEAD PROSTITUTES LIES IN THOSE DOLLS.

WE ARE *BARRED* FROM THE GATES OF *HEAVEN,* SHE SAID.

KILL THEM. PLEASE. SHE SAID.

LONE WOLF AND CUB...

NEXT MONTH

LONE WOLF and CUB

by
KAZUO KOIKE
and
GOSEKI KOJIMA

introduction by
FRANK MILLER

第 8 巻

FIRST PUBLISHING $2.50 U.S. $3.50 CANADA

© 1987 FIRST COMICS, INC. AND GLOBAL COMMUNICATIONS CORP.

They say that one who would catch the tiger's cub must enter the lair of the tiger. But what happens when the Lone Wolf uses his own cub as bait to lure the tiger out of his lair? Itto Ogami and his infant son Daigoro head straight into the jaws of the tiger and a "Dead End."

来月